Sarah Parrish ♡

MUSICAL THEATRE COLLECTION
FOR
YOUNG WOMEN SINGERS

Hal Leonard Europe
Distributed by Music Sales

Exclusive Distributors:
Music Sales Limited
8/9 Frith Street, London W1D 3JB, England.
Music Sales Pty Limited
120 Rothschild Avenue, Rosebery, NSW 2018, Australia.

Order No. HLE90001476
ISBN 0-7119-8728-9
This book © Copyright 2002 by Hal Leonard Europe

Cover design Chloë Alexander
Cover photograph courtesy Rex Features
Printed in the USA

Your Guarantee of Quality
As publishers, we strive to produce every book to the highest
commercial standards.
The book has been carefully designed to minimise awkward
page turns and to make playing from it a real pleasure.
Throughout, the printing and binding have been planned to ensure a
sturdy, attractive publication which should give years of enjoyment.
If your copy fails to meet our high standards, please inform us
and we will gladly replace it.

www.musicsales.com

ADELAIDE'S LAMENT
from GUYS AND DOLLS

By FRANK LOESSER

G/B
(2nd time accel.)
C#9b5
C9
fect-ing the up - per res - pir - a - tor - y tract. In
volv-ing the eye, the ear, and the nose, and throat. In
(2nd time accel.)
F6
A7
Bb6
Gm7b5
oth - er words, just from wait - ing a - round for that plain lit - tle band of gold A
oth - er words, just from wor - ry - ing wheth - er the wed-ding is on or off A
F/C
Gm7
C7
F6
F9
per - son can de - vel - op a cold. You can
per - son can de - vel - op a cough. You can
B6
A#m7
A#dim7
spray her wher - ev - er you fig - ure the strep - to - coc - ci lurk, You can
feed her all day with the Vi - ta - min A and the Bro - mo Fizz But the

AS LONG AS HE NEEDS ME

from the Columbia Pictures - Romulus Motion Picture Production of Lionel Bart's OLIVER!

Words and Music by
LIONEL BART

BEAUTY AND THE BEAST
from Walt Disney's BEAUTY AND THE BEAST

Lyrics by HOWARD ASHMAN
Music by ALAN MENKEN

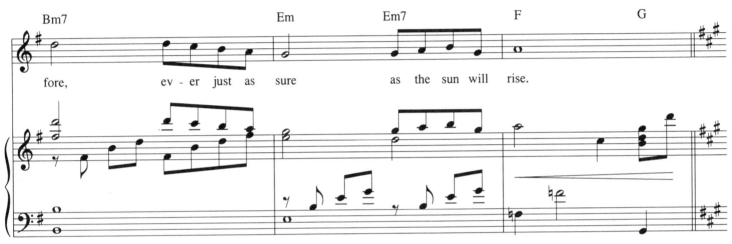

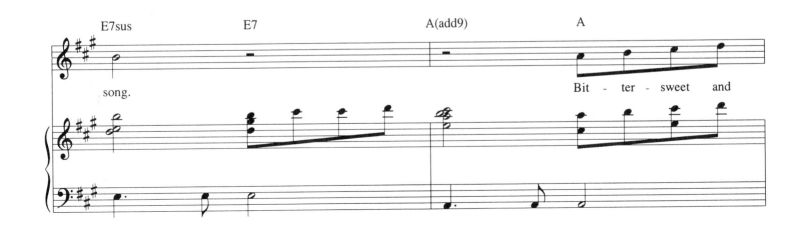

Tale as old as time, song as old as

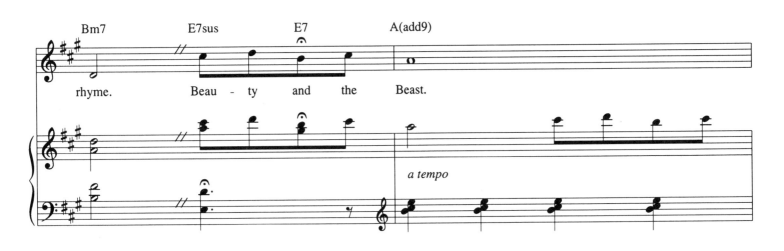

rhyme. Beau - ty and the Beast.

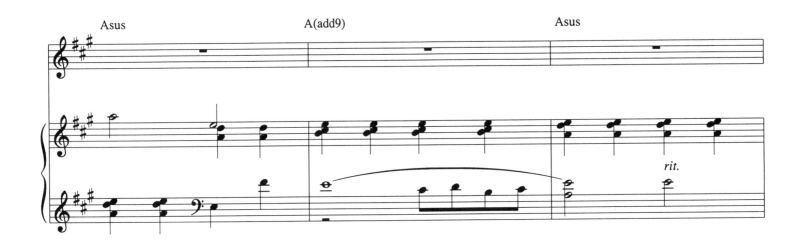

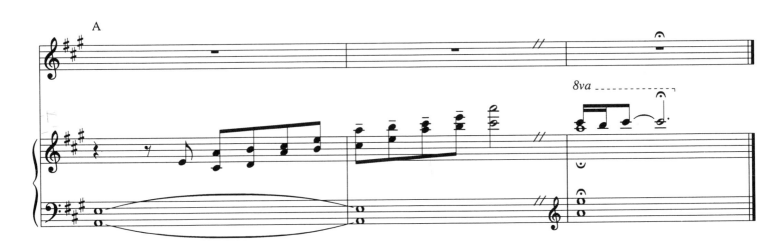

BELLE
(Reprise)
from Walt Disney's BEAUTY AND THE BEAST

Lyrics by HOWARD ASHMAN
Music by ALAN MENKEN

A BUSHEL AND A PECK
from GUYS AND DOLLS

By FRANK LOESSER

Light Bounce Tempo

Can You Feel The Love Tonight

from Walt Disney Pictures' THE LION KING

Music by ELTON JOHN
Lyrics by TIM RICE

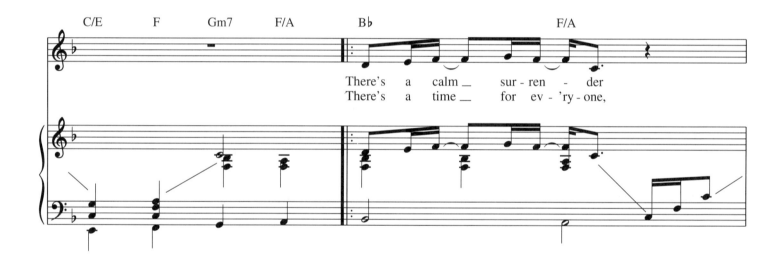

There's a calm __ sur - ren - der
There's a time __ for ev - 'ry - one,

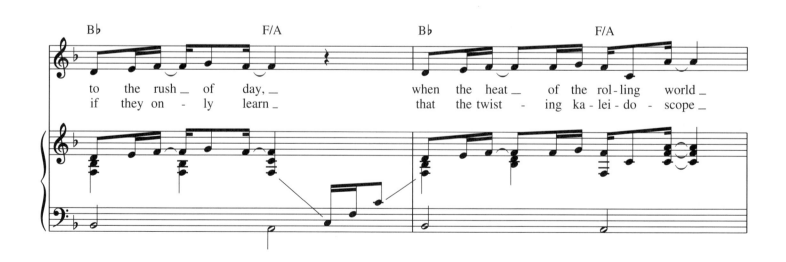

to the rush __ of day, __ when the heat __ of the rol - ling world __
if they on - ly learn __ that the twist - ing ka - lei - do - scope __

A COCKEYED OPTIMIST
from SOUTH PACIFIC

Lyrics by OSCAR HAMMERSTEIN II
Music by RICHARD RODGERS

COLORS OF THE WIND
from Walt Disney's POCAHONTAS

Music by ALAN MENKEN
Lyrics by STEPHEN SCHWARTZ

DIAMONDS ARE A GIRL'S BEST FRIEND

from GENTLEMEN PREFER BLONDES

Words by LEO ROBIN
Music by JULE STYNE

FEED THE BIRDS
from Walt Disney's MARY POPPINS

Words and Music by RICHARD M. SHERMAN
and ROBERT B. SHERMAN

see it, you know they are smil-ing Each time some-one shows that he

cares._____ Though____ her words are sim-ple____ and few,

Lis-ten,____ lis-ten,____she's call-ing to you: "Feed____ the birds,

tup-pence____ a bag, Tup-pence,____ tup-pence,____ tup-pence____ a bag."

GOD HELP THE OUTCASTS
from Walt Disney's THE HUNCHBACK OF NOTRE DAME

Music by ALAN MENKEN
Lyrics by STEPHEN SCHWARTZ

Slowly

I don't know if You can hear me or if You're e-ven there. I don't know if You will

lis - ten to a hum - ble prayer. They tell me I am just an

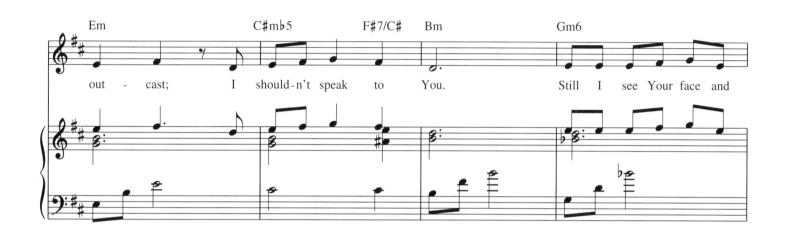

out - cast; I should-n't speak to You. Still I see Your face and

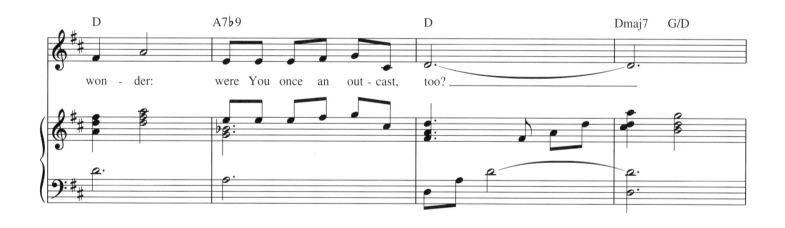

won - der: were You once an out - cast, too? _____

God help the out - casts
I ask for noth - ing,

GOODNIGHT, MY SOMEONE
from Meredith Willson's THE MUSIC MAN

By MEREDITH WILLSON

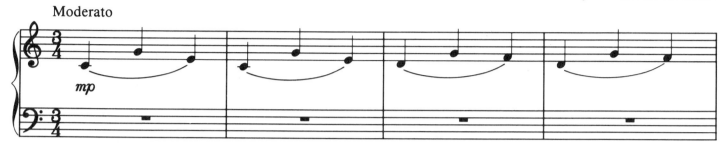

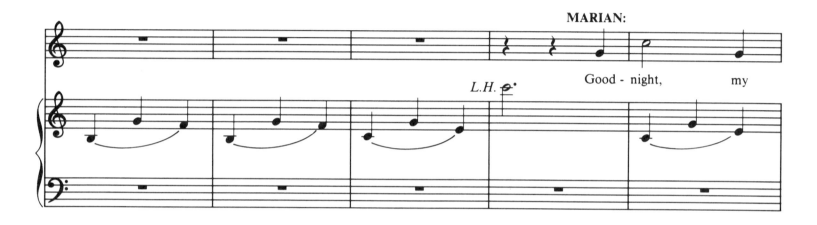

light for good-night, my love, for good-night._____ Sweet

dreams be yours, dear, if dreams there be; Sweet dreams to

car - ry you close to me. I wish they may, and I

wish they might. Now good-night, my some - one, good - night._____

Poco mosso

True love can be whis-pered from heart to heart, when lov-ers are part-ed they say. But I must de-pend on a wish and a star, as long as my heart does-n't know who you are. Sweet dreams be yours, dear, if dreams there

HONEY BUN
from SOUTH PACIFIC

Lyrics by OSCAR HAMMERSTEIN II
Music by RICHARD RODGERS

Lyrics:

My doll is as dain-ty as a spar-row, _____ Her fig-ure is some-thing to ap-plaud. Where she's nar-row she's nar-row as an ar-row, _____ and she's broad where a broad should be broad. _____

58

I ENJOY BEING A GIRL
from FLOWER DRUM SONG

Lyrics by OSCAR HAMMERSTEIN II
Music by RICHARD RODGERS

I HAVE CONFIDENCE
from THE SOUND OF MUSIC

Music and Lyrics by
RICHARD RODGERS

Moderato (rubato)

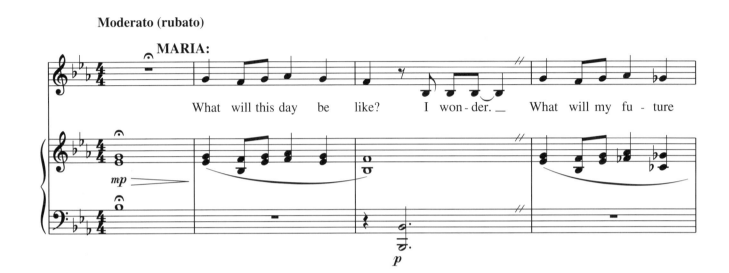

Più mosso

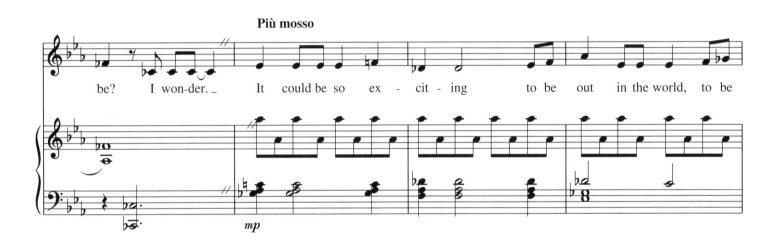

I'll do bet-ter than my best. _____ I have con - fi - dence they'll put me to the test, But I'll make them see I have con - fi - dence in me. Some - how I will im - press them. _____ I will be firm but kind. _____ And all those chil - dren,

Con moto

I have con-fi-dence in sun - shine,____

I have con-fi-dence in rain._____ I have con-fi-dence that

spring will come a - gain. Be - sides which, you see, I have con-fi-dence in me.

Strength does - n't lie in num - bers,____ Strength does - n't lie in

I WON'T SAY
(I'm in Love)
from HERCULES

Music by ALAN MENKEN
Lyrics by DAVID ZIPPEL

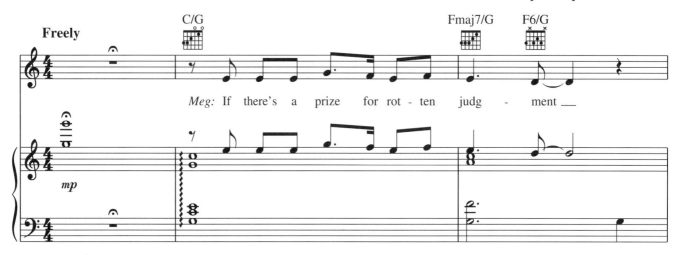

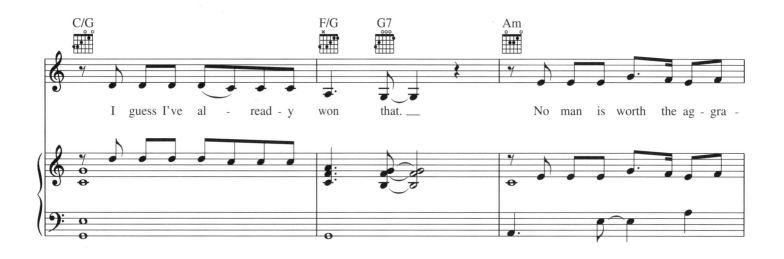

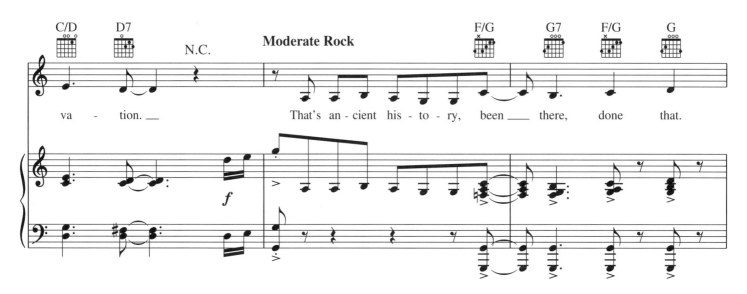

I'M GONNA WASH THAT MAN RIGHT OUTA MY HAIR

from SOUTH PACIFIC

Lyrics by OSCAR HAMMERSTEIN II
Music by RICHARD RODGERS

*This is changed to "she" when sung by other characters.

out - a my arms, __ I'm gon - na wave that man right out - a my arms, __ I'm gon - na
out - a my arms, __ I went and waved that man right out - a my arms, __ I went and

wave that man right out - a my arms, __ And send him on his
waved that man right out - a my arms, __ And sent him on his

NURSES:

way. _____
way. _____

Don't try to patch it up, Tear it up, tear it up!

NELLIE: NURSES: NELLIE:

Wash him out, dry him out, Push him out, fly him out, Can - cel him _____ and let him

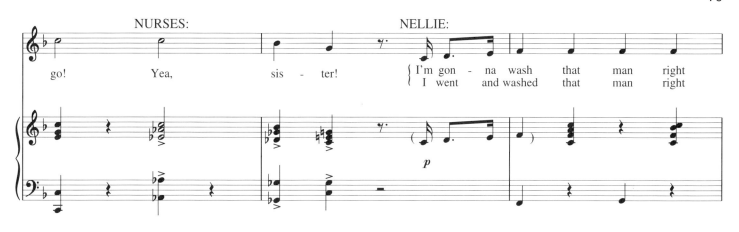

NURSES: NELLIE:

go!   Yea,   sis - ter!   I'm gon - na wash that man right
I went and washed that man right

out - a my hair, __ I'm gon - na wash that man right out - a my hair, __ I'm gon - na
out - a my hair, __ I went and washed that man right out - a my hair, __ I went and

To Coda ⊕

wash that man right out - a my hair __ And send him on his way!   If the
washed that man right out - a my hair __ And

(♩. = ♩)

man don't un - der - stand you, _____ If you fly on sep' - rate beams,

Waste no time! __ Make a change, __ Ride that man right off your range, __

NURSES:

Rub him out - a the roll call _____ And drum him out - a your dreams! _____ Oh

ho! _____ If you laugh at dif - f'rent com - ics, _____ If you root for dif - f'rent

teams, Waste no time, __ Weep no more, __ Show him what the door is for! __

I'LL KNOW
from GUYS AND DOLLS

By FRANK LOESSER

I'VE NEVER BEEN IN LOVE BEFORE

from GUYS AND DOLLS

Tune Uke
A D F♯ B

By FRANK LOESSER

IN MY LIFE
from LES MISÉRABLES

Music by CLAUDE-MICHEL SCHÖNBERG
Lyrics by HERBERT KRETZMER
Original Text by ALAIN BOUBLIL and JEAN-MARC NATEL

way, _____ Wait-ing for me; Does he know_ I'm a-live?_ Do I know _ if he's

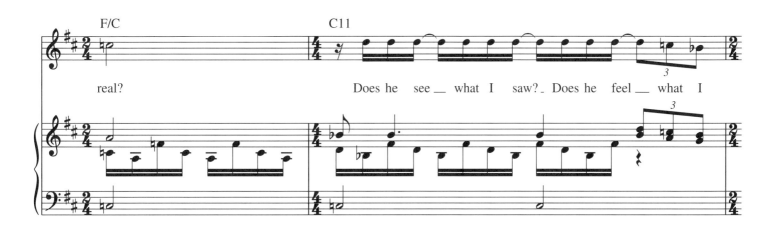

real? Does he see _ what I saw?_ Does he feel _ what I

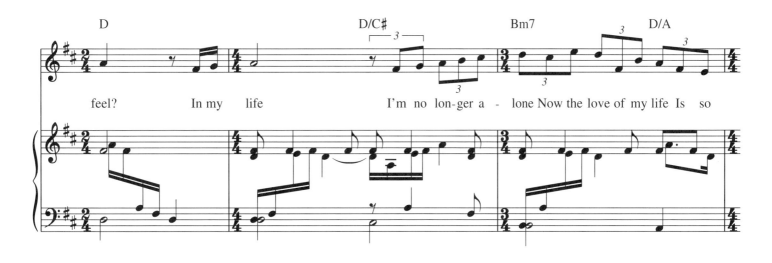

feel? In my life I'm no lon-ger a - lone Now the love of my life Is so

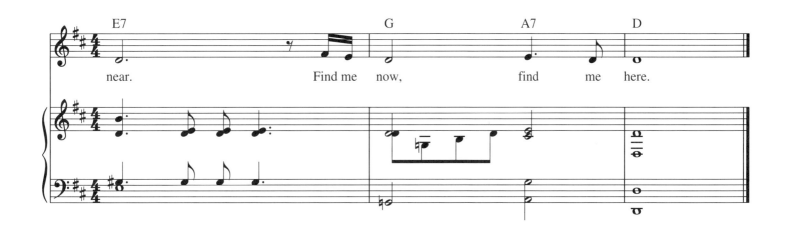

near. Find me now, find me here.

IN MY OWN LITTLE CORNER
from CINDERELLA

Lyrics by OSCAR HAMMERSTEIN II
Music by RICHARD RODGERS

IT MIGHT AS WELL BE SPRING

from STATE FAIR

Lyrics by OSCAR HAMMERSTEIN II
Music by RICHARD RODGERS

The things I used to like I don't like an-y-more. I want a lot of oth-er things I've

nev-er had be-fore. It's just like moth-er says, I "sit a - round and mope" pre-

tend-ing I am won-der-ful and know-ing I'm a dope. _____ I'm as

MANY A NEW DAY
from OKLAHOMA!

Lyrics by OSCAR HAMMERSTEIN II
Music by RICHARD RODGERS

ON MY OWN
from LES MISÉRABLES

Music by CLAUDE-MICHEL SCHONBERG
Lyrics by ALAIN BOUBLIL, HERBERT KRETZMER, JOHN CAIRD,
TREVOR NUNN and JEAN-MARC NATEL

MY FAVORITE THINGS
from THE SOUND OF MUSIC

Lyrics by OSCAR HAMMERSTEIN II
Music by RICHARD RODGERS

ONCE YOU LOSE YOUR HEART

from ME AND MY GIRL

Words and Music by
NOEL GAY

PEOPLE WILL SAY WE'RE IN LOVE
from OKLAHOMA!

Lyrics by OSCAR HAMMERSTEIN II
Music by RICHARD RODGERS

OUT OF MY DREAMS
from OKLAHOMA!

Lyrics by OSCAR HAMMERSTEIN II
Music by RICHARD RODGERS

Gm6　　　　A7　　　　Dm

You'll　　be　　real,

Fm6/Ab　　　　C　　　　G7

real　as　the　white　moon　light - ing　the

C　　　　　　　　Cdim

blue.

C7　　　　　　　　D.S. al Fine

PART OF YOUR WORLD
from Walt Disney's THE LITTLE MERMAID

Lyrics by HOWARD ASHMAN
Music by ALAN MENKEN

Moderately bright

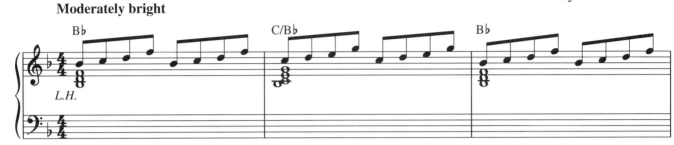

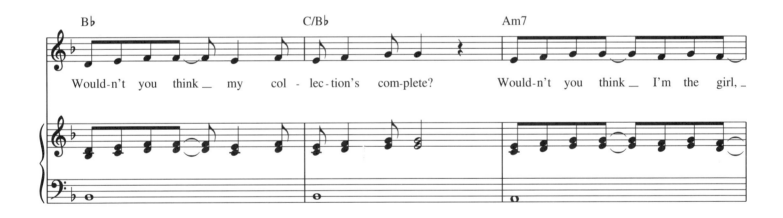

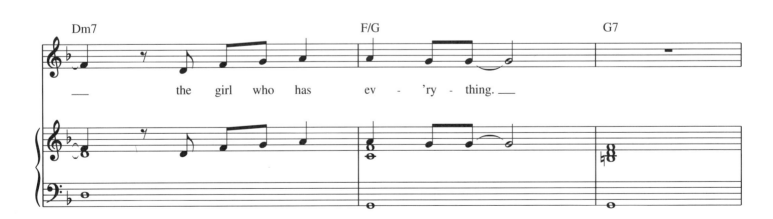

Look at this trove, _ treas-ures un-told. _ How man-y won-ders can

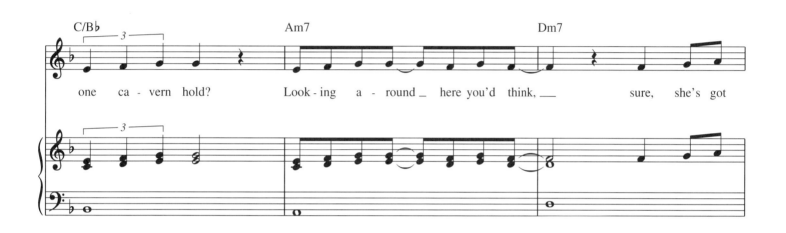

one ca-vern hold? Look-ing a-round _ here you'd think, __ sure, she's got

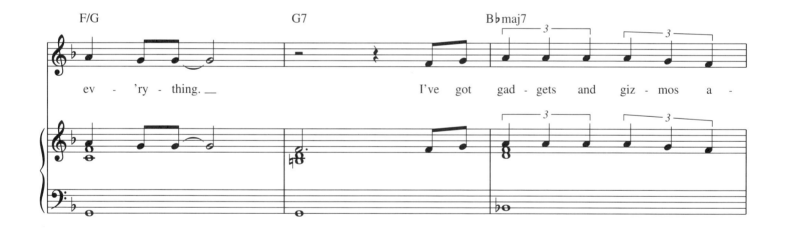

ev - 'ry - thing. _ I've got gad-gets and giz-mos a-

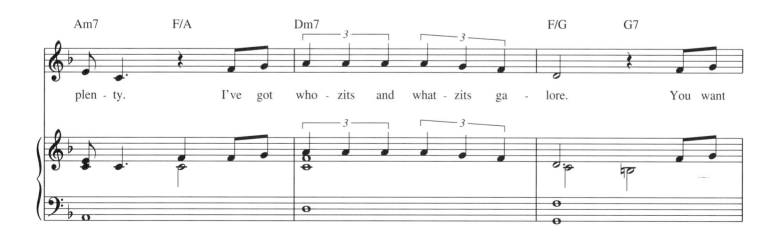

plen-ty. I've got who-zits and what-zits ga-lore. You want

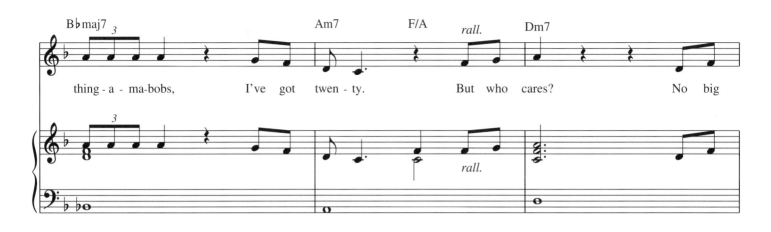

thing-a-ma-bobs, I've got twen-ty. But who cares? No big

deal. I want more.

I wan-na be ____ where the peo-ple are. I wan-na see ____ wan-na

see 'em danc - in', walk-in' a - round ___ on those, what-d-ya call ___ 'em, oh

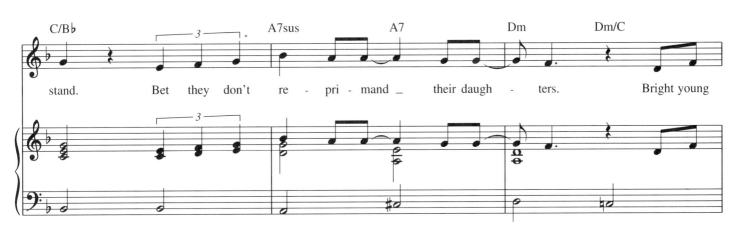

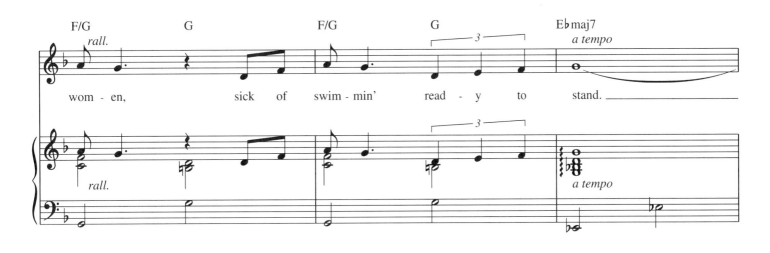

REFLECTION
from Walt Disney Pictures' MULAN

Music by MATTHEW WILDER
Lyrics by DAVID ZIPPEL

SIXTEEN GOING ON SEVENTEEN
from THE SOUND OF MUSIC

Lyrics by OSCAR HAMMERSTEIN II
Music by RICHARD RODGERS

STEPSISTERS'S LAMENT
from CINDERELLA

Lyrics by OSCAR HAMMERSTEIN II
Music by RICHARD RODGERS

TILL THERE WAS YOU

from Meredith Willson's THE MUSIC MAN

By MEREDITH WILLSON

UNEXPECTED SONG
from SONG AND DANCE

Music by ANDREW LLOYD WEBBER
Lyrics by DON BLACK